Published by Hear Our Voice LLC
www.hearourvoicellc.com

Written by Amy G. Strayer
Illustrated by Stacy Brevard-Mays

Dedication

Marsha Gregory Strayer 1943 - 2021

A selfless Mom, wife, grandma, sister, aunt, daughter, mamma Strayer and friend.

If you knew her you loved her ... If she loved you, you never doubted it.

If you mentioned it in front of her ... She always remembered.

She listened to listen ... And called later to hear more.

The other half of the strength of our family and traditions .... The love of friends who became family

We miss you everyday Mom

This book belongs to

_____

Written by: Amy G. Strayer
Illustrated by: Stacy Brevard-Mays

A TRIP TO THE DOCTOR

The Pelican's Pouch Series

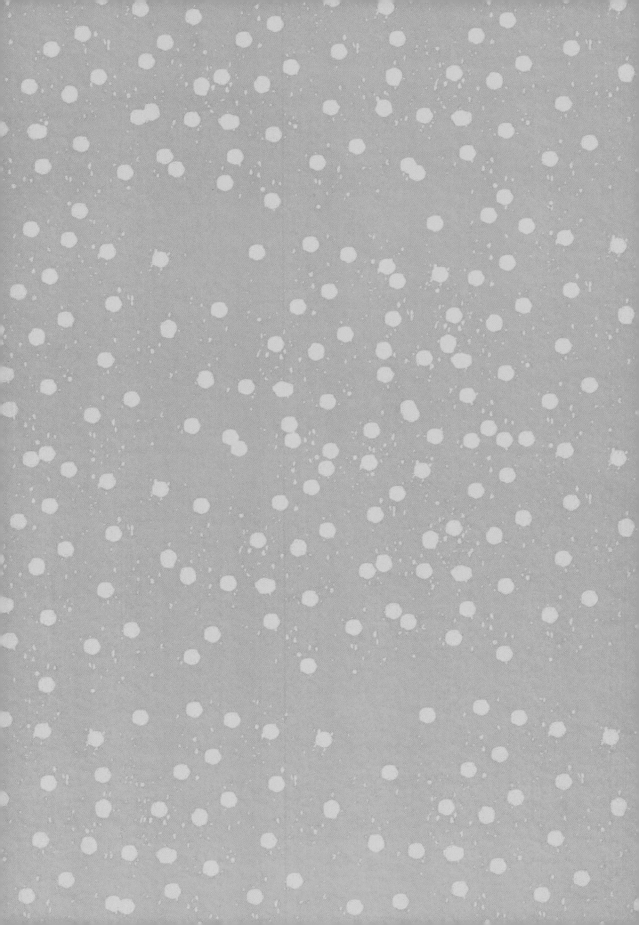

I told them it hurt,
And I wasn't sure why.
They wrote down what I said,
Through their smile was a sigh.

Next step is the)ctor, Now climb to bed." Tucked into the covers, ith a gentle kiss on the head.

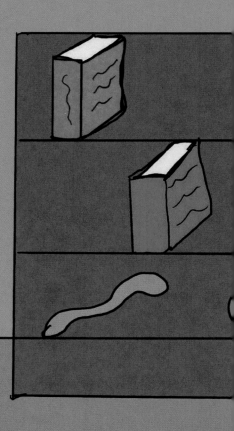

I tossed and I turned, Threw the pillows around. Turned the light right back on, And made not a sound.

I tossed and I turned, Threw the pillows around. Turned the light right back on, And made not a sound.

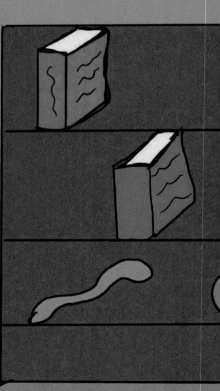

What will they do?
What will they say?
Should I be scared?
Can someone
please stay?

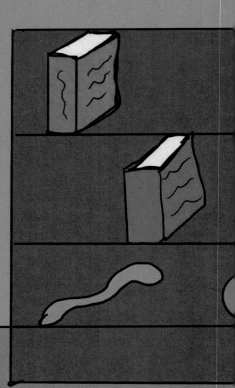

Morning came quickly, No breakfast today, Got dressed, brushed my teeth, And we're all on our way.

Pulled into the lot, Found a spot by the door.. This building is huge, I don't need to see more.

Out of the car, And up the long walk. Please hold onto my hand, But please do not talk. 🤫

I have questions
and fears, There is
so much to see.
Doctors and nurses,
Are they all here
for me?

Up to the window, Birthdate and name. Now please have a seat, Read a book, play a game.

Some advice from a Pelican, Some friends and the beach. The things that I love, I want one of each.

Relax, take a breath,
Be brave and be strong.
First is your temperature,
This lists not too long.

Sit in the chair, Feet flat on the floor. Now lift up your tongue, There isn't much more.

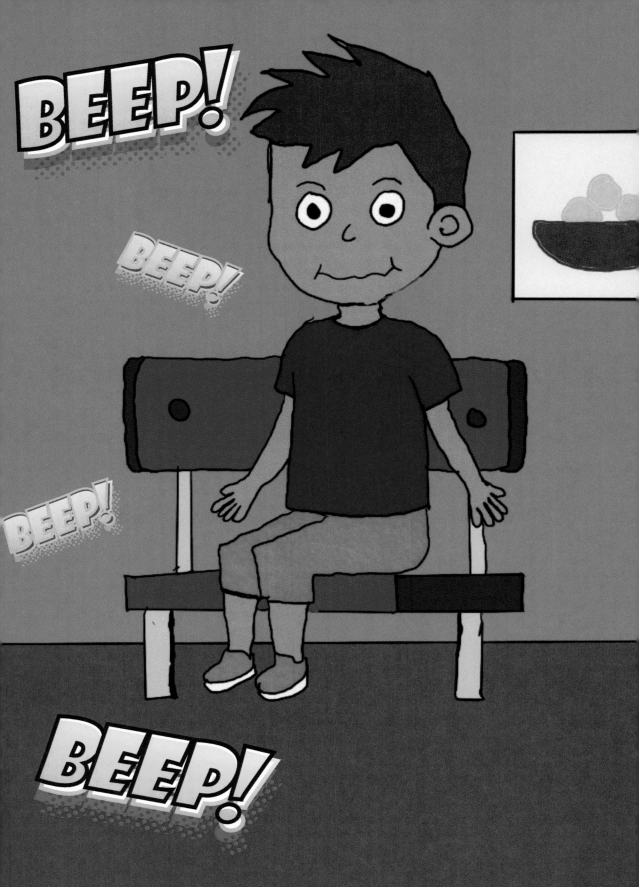

Next comes the beep,
Temperature check
is complete. Step two
is up next, You can
stay in this seat.

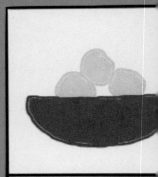

Blood pressure next,
So roll up your sleeve.
This step is easy,
You're doing great I
believe.

Two basic things, A gauge and a cuff. They'll start pumping the ball, 'Til the cuff's had enough.

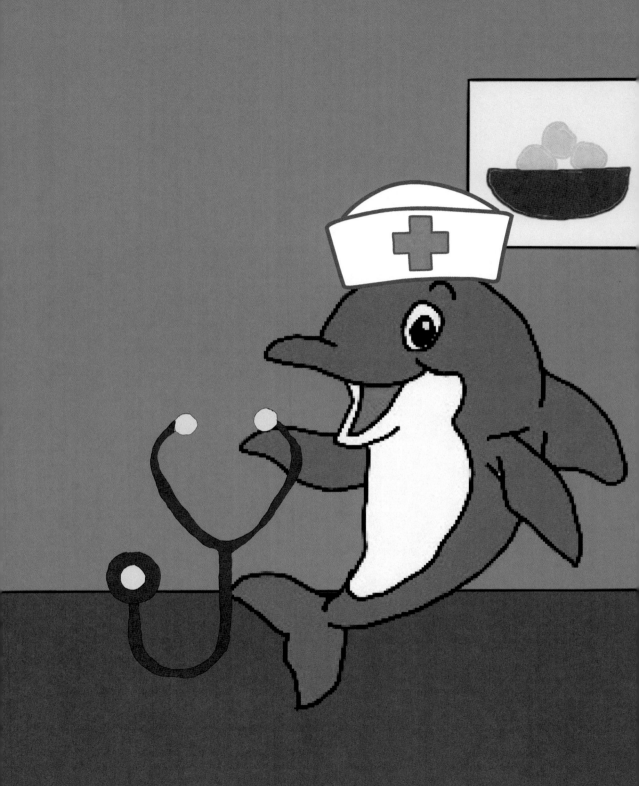

A stethoscope's next, Might be cold to your arm. It helps give them info, No need for alarm.

Turning the valve,
Letting all the air
free. They'll unwrap
the cuff, On to step
three.

Step three is quite
easy, And has to do
with the heart.
Stethoscope again,
And we're ready to
start.

For this please be quiet, Sit tall and breathe deep.. Your heart beats are heard, You can't say a peep.

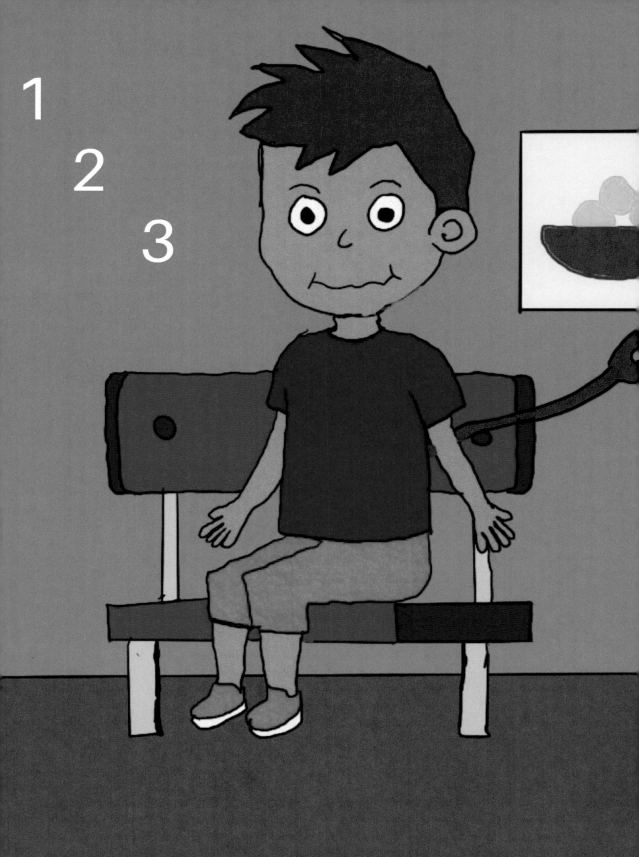

First in the front, One,
two, breathe and hold.
Next to the back, Do
exactly as your told.

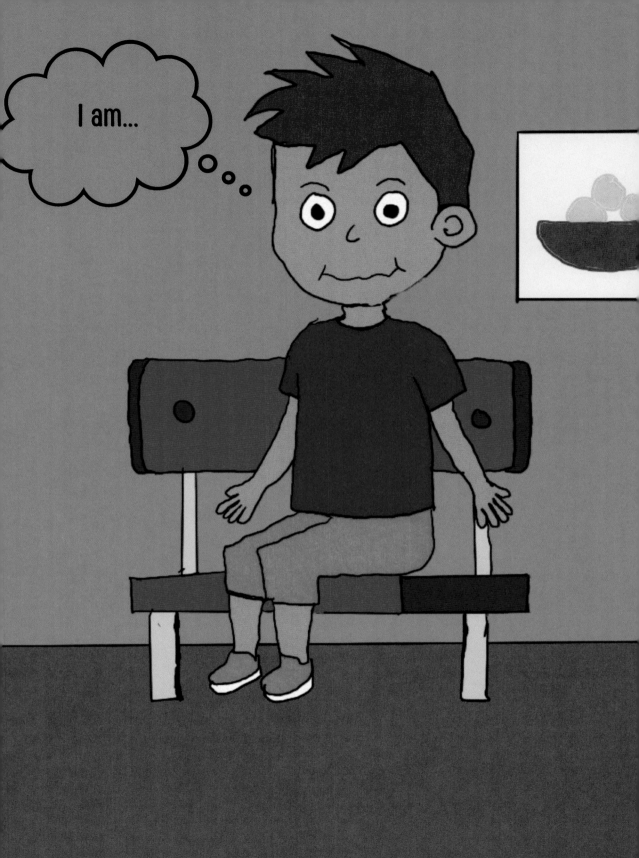

Next on the list, Is step four and the best. You can tell all about YOU, No need to be stressed.

Questions about pain,
And the places it hurts.
Point to them now, Tell
them which is the
worst.

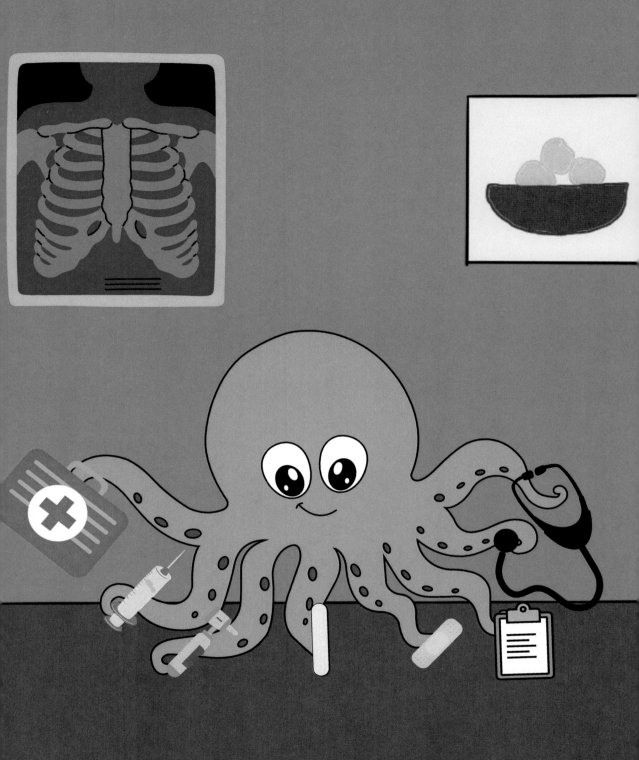

The doctor takes notes, About all that you say. Some meds and advice, To help you get better and play.

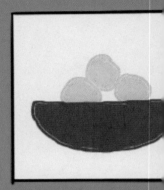

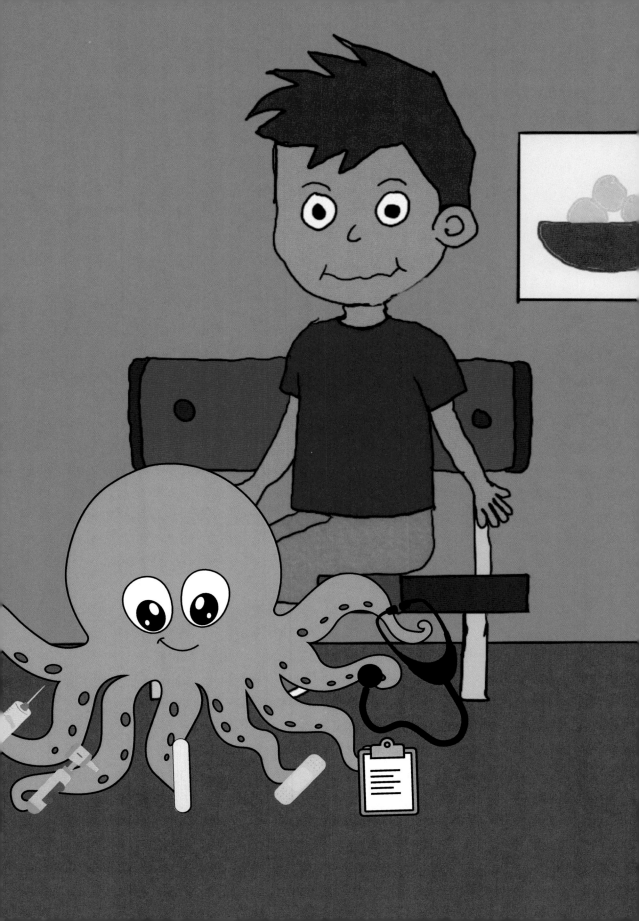

A review of your visit,
The notes and the
tests. Let's all sit and
talk, And go over the
rest.

More sleep or some meds And maybe a shot, It might be more tests, But whatever they've got....

You've made some new friends. The Pelican and fish. And they will be with you, However you wish.

Journal Your Visit

Journal Your Visit

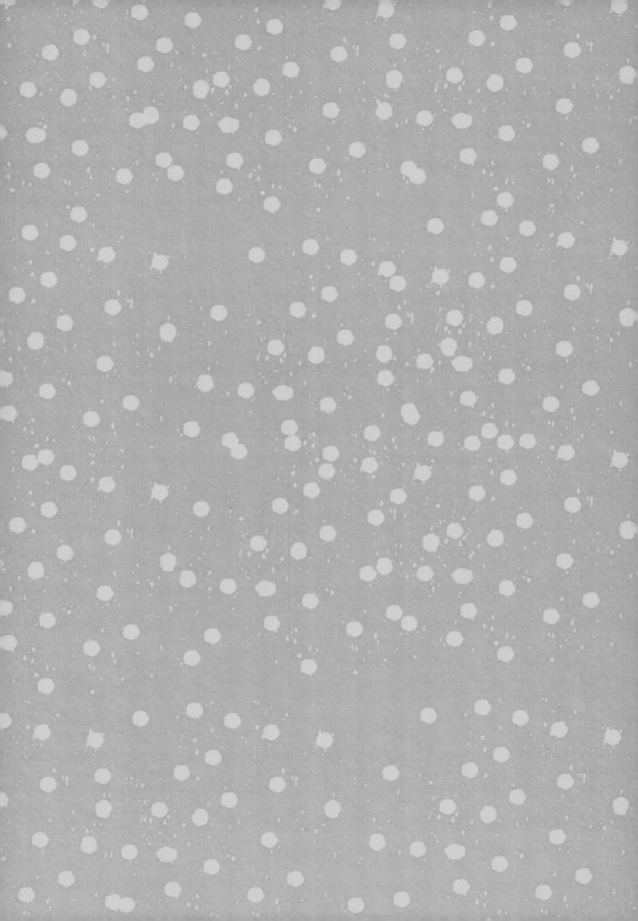

Pelicans Pouch - A Trip to the Doctor

```
J V Q G A U G E C M P V X M E
A J U M N A K X R B F G G I Y
A R F N B U H H Z O U I O F X
X R W U Q C C C U P U A S U U
K N E Z U B D D U J J L Q H D
W I N D P R R D F F R Y Z C O
D B E F H E M O A G F P O R X
P Z S N G A Q C W S H E F P N
M V Q G G T Y T D Z H L N V A
X T A S U H S O H F H I U S E
C E P L P A G R R Y X C J V G
Z S L N V S C Z J N I A Y B M
C T A M G E K E C Q T N D T E
F H A J L M H Y Z G S H O T D
N U R S E P W V O U T O O J S
```

Pelican	Breath	Doctor	Cuff
Nurse	Gauge	Valve	Shot
Fish	Meds	Test	

Made in the USA
Monee, IL
09 August 2023

3b97adf6-8654-4f2a-b996-ab49d7b3955aR01